HODDER HOME LEARNING

Weights and Measures

AGE 5-7

Rhona Whiteford and Jim Fitzsimmons
Illustrated by Sascha Lipscomb

As a parent, you can play an important part in your child's education by your interest and encouragement. This book is designed to help your child become more confident in the vital mathematical skills of weighing and measuring. There are six sections, each with a short test.

How to help your child

- Keep sessions short and regular. Your child will learn more if you approach the exercises as an enjoyable challenge, rather than an unpleasant chore.

- Let your child join in with any measuring jobs in the home, like cooking. If you can, use a set of pan scales instead of a spring balance so that your child will see the weights balance.

- Maths is something we use every day – to estimate distances, weights and sizes of objects. Regular practice builds up familiarity and confidence for both you and your child.

- Build up your child's confidence by offering lots of praise and encouragement. Rather than simply pointing out that an answer is wrong, you could say, 'You were almost right. Let's try again together!'

- Don't treat the tests too formally. You can keep a running total of results on the chart on page 23. When the book is completed you can award the certificate to your child. A sense of achievement is a great motivator!

Hodder Children's Books

NATIONAL CONFEDERATION OF · PARENT TEACHER ASSOCIATIONS

The only home learning programme supported by the NCPTA

Weighing

We need to weigh things to find out how heavy they are. Sometimes we can guess which is the heaviest thing just by looking.

Look at these pictures and tick the one in each box which you think might be heavier in real life:

car ✓   flower ☐

boy ☐   house ✓

mouse ☐   pig ☐

Draw something heavier than this:

Draw something lighter than this:

Draw something heavier than you:

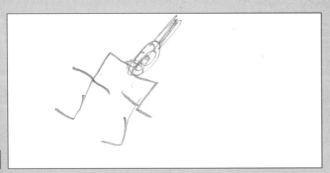

Draw something lighter than you:

Who is heavier, Jim or Sally?

Who is lighter, Susan or Peter?

Who weighs more, Sally or Jim?

Who weighs less, Ben or Alice?

Is Peter heavier than Susan?

Look at these balances:

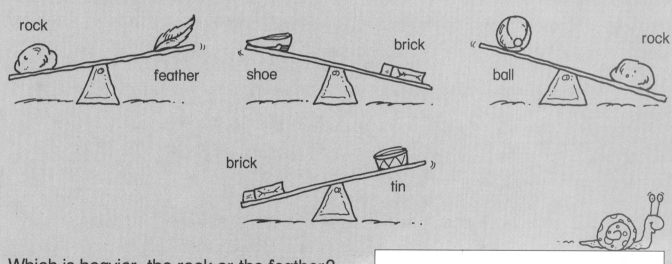

rock   feather

shoe   brick

ball   rock

brick   tin

Which is heavier, the rock or the feather?

Which weighs more, the shoe or the brick?

Which is lighter, the ball or the rock?

Which weighs less, the brick or the tin?

Is the shoe lighter than the brick?

3

Weighing things

You will need
a balance or
a set of
pan scales.

Choose some things to balance with. You could use:

marbles

dried peas

1p coins

building blocks
(all the same size)

We can use these as **units of measurement.**

Take a small book and place it on one pan of the balance. This pan goes down.
Now choose one of the units of measurement, such as marbles, and start putting
these into the other pan of the balance. Do this until both pans are level once more.
Count how many units it took to balance the book.

For example

It takes | 36 marbles |

to balance my book.

Do this for 4 different objects. Use the same unit of measurement each time.

Object		It takes			to balance.
Object		It takes			to balance.
Object		It takes			to balance.
Object		It takes			to balance.

The heaviest object is _____. The lightest object is _____

Choosing the best units

Choose two objects to weigh.

Object [   ]

It takes [ ] dried peas [ ] 1p coins [ ] building blocks [ ] marbles to balance.

Object [   ]

It takes [ ] dried peas [ ] 1p coins [ ] building blocks [ ] marbles to balance.

Which object is heavier? [   ]

Which unit of measurement was easiest to use? [   ]

Why was it the easiest? [   ]

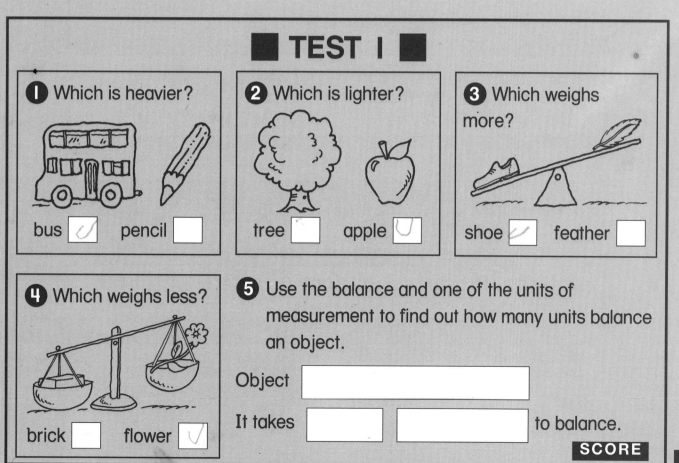

■ TEST 1 ■

1 Which is heavier?

bus [✓]   pencil [ ]

2 Which is lighter?

tree [ ]   apple [✓]

3 Which weighs more?

shoe [✓]   feather [ ]

4 Which weighs less?

brick [ ]   flower [✓]

5 Use the balance and one of the units of measurement to find out how many units balance an object.

Object [   ]

It takes [   ] [   ] to balance.

Estimating and weighing

As you get used to balancing things, you can start to guess how many units it will take to balance different objects.

Take a small tin from the grocery cupboard. Choose a unit of measurement, then estimate or guess how many units will balance the tin. Write the name of the **Object** first, then write your guess or **Estimate** in the next column. Use the balance to check how many units actually balance the tin. Write this number in the **Weight** column. If your estimate was higher or more than the weight, put a tick in the **More** column. If it was lower, or less, put a tick in the **Less** column.

Choose another 3 objects and complete the table using the same units of measurement each time.

3   2

Object	Estimate	Weight	More	Less
tin	600g	230g	✓	
RICE	500g	100g	✓✓	
PEPPER				

Now choose a different **unit of measurement** and **estimate** and **weigh the same four objects.** On the chart, fill in the **More** and **Less** columns as before.

Object	Estimate	Weight	More	Less
tin				

Which was the best unit for weighing?

Why was it the best?

■ TEST 2 ■

You will need 100 paper-clips. Make two sets of 50. Take one set of 50 paper-clips and hold them in one hand. Try to find 4 things which each weigh less than 50 paper-clips. Write the names of these things on the table below. Then use the balance to check and complete the table.

	Object	Estimate	Weight	More	Less
1					
2					
3					
4					

Next hold the 100 paper-clips in one hand and try to find four more things which each weigh more than 50 paper-clips but less than 100 paper-clips.
Use the balance to check and complete this table.

	Object	Estimate	Weight	More	Less
5					
6					
7					
8					

Score 1 point for each item correctly placed in each table.

SCORE

8

Standard units for weighing

Using different units of measurement to weigh the same thing gives different results, so it can be helpful to use a standard unit of measurement. Using a standard unit means we can easily compare the weights of different things.

The weight of something is usually measured in grams.

If something weighs **3 grams** we can write it as **3g**.

Look for these packages in the cupboard. Write the weights as shown on the labels.

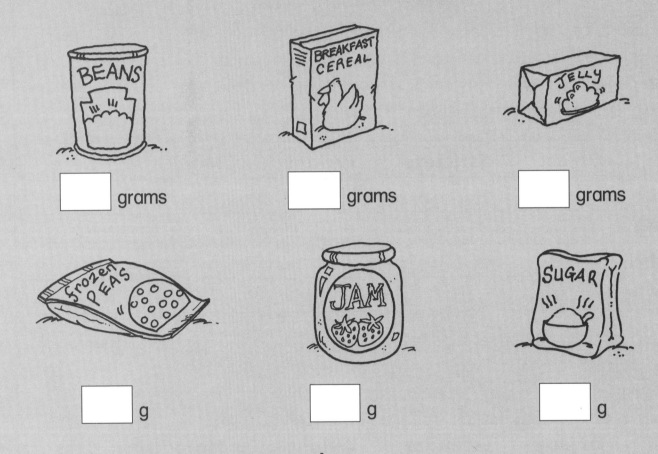

[   ] grams   [   ] grams   [   ] grams

[   ] g   [   ] g   [   ] g

Sometimes on large packages we see **kg**.

kg stands for **kilogram. There are 1000 grams in a kilogram.**

Find 3 things which come in packs weighing **1 kg** or more. Look in your grocery cupboard, or in the supermarket when you next visit.

1 [   ]   **2** [   ]   **3** [   ]

Using the kilogram

I pack of butter weighs **250 g**, so 4 packs of butter will weigh
4 x 250 g = 1000 g = I kg.

Put four packs of butter in a plastic bag and hold it in one hand. Now compare the weight with the other things. You will need some objects like these:

a brick

a large book

a packet of sugar

a rock

a bag of sand

Choose 3 objects and estimate if each one weighs **more than a kilogram, less than a kilogram** or **about the same as a kilogram**. Fill in your answers below.

I estimate the [   ] weighs [   ] a kilogram.

I estimate the [   ] weighs [   ] a kilogram.

I estimate the [   ] weighs [   ] a kilogram.

Now use a balance.

Put the packs of butter in one pan and place one of the objects in the other pan to find out if it weighs **more than**, **less than** or **about the same as** a kilogram. Now do the same with the other two objects and fill in your answers below.

The [   ] weighs [   ] a kilogram.

The [   ] weighs [   ] a kilogram.

The [   ] weighs [   ] a kilogram.

By using only 2 of the packs of butter you will get a **half kilogram**. Repeat the above activity to estimate and check the weight of objects like these:

a small book

a shoe

a tape measure

a box of crayons

Weighing in grams – reading the scales

Practise weighing different things using a set of kitchen scales.

When an object is placed in the dish on top of the scales its weight presses down on a spring which moves the pointer on the dial. The pointer tells you the weight.

Weigh these things carefully:

6 tea bags weigh [   ] g   4 tomatoes weigh [   ] g

3 potatoes weigh [   ] g   2 oranges weigh [   ] g

Now try to weigh out the following amounts:

Weigh out 5 g of peas.   Weigh out 8 g of pasta.

Weigh out 10 g of sugar.   Weigh out 12 g of breakfast cereal.

It is important to weigh out ingredients accurately when following a recipe. Here is one for fruit bars. Ask an adult to help you weigh out all the ingredients and follow the instructions for a delicious treat.

Ingredients

200 g digestive biscuits

50 g butter or margarine

50 g golden treacle

100 g seedless raisins

50 g mixed peel, finely chopped

Grated rind of 1 orange

A little glacé icing

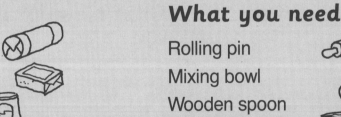

What you need

Rolling pin

Mixing bowl

Wooden spoon

Saucepan

20 cm square tin
  which has been greased

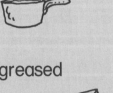

What you do

Roll and crush the biscuits with the rolling pin until they are
fine crumbs.

Put them in the mixing bowl.

Melt the butter and treacle in the saucepan and pour over
the crumbs.

Mix well with the wooden spoon until they are absorbed.

Add the orange rind, raisins and mixed peel and mix again.

Press the mixture into the greased tin.

Press firmly down and leave to set overnight.

When set, top with a little icing and cut into finger-sized bars.

■ TEST 3 ■

Using the kitchen scales

1 Weigh 6 large potatoes. [ ] g

2 Weigh 3 apples. [ ] g

3 Weigh 4 carrots. [ ] g

4 Weigh out 10 g rice.

5 Weigh out 12 g pasta.

6 Weigh out 16 g lentils.

Use the bathroom scales to weigh 4 members of your family or friends.

	Name		
7		kg	g
8		kg	g
9		kg	g
10		kg	g

Score 1 point for each one weighed correctly.

Measuring length

It's often useful to be able to measure the length of something. We can compare the lengths of things in different ways.

Label the longer snake.

Label the shorter car.

Label the taller tree.

Label the smaller boy.

Draw pictures of things that are taller than you:

Draw pictures of things that are shorter than you:

Long ago, people used different parts of the body to measure length with.
Here are some examples:

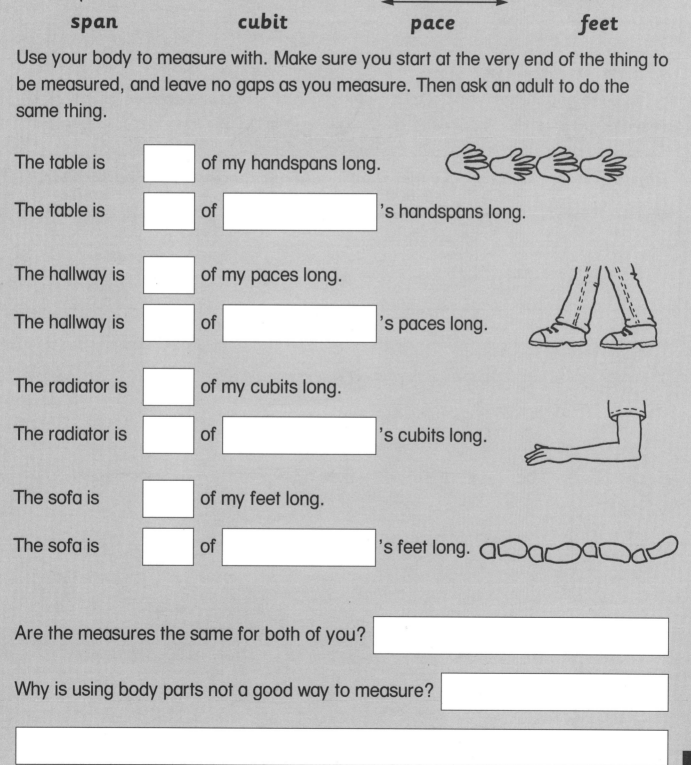

span   **cubit**   **pace**   **feet**

Use your body to measure with. Make sure you start at the very end of the thing to be measured, and leave no gaps as you measure. Then ask an adult to do the same thing.

The table is ☐ of my handspans long.

The table is ☐ of ☐ 's handspans long.

The hallway is ☐ of my paces long.

The hallway is ☐ of ☐ 's paces long.

The radiator is ☐ of my cubits long.

The radiator is ☐ of ☐ 's cubits long.

The sofa is ☐ of my feet long.

The sofa is ☐ of ☐ 's feet long.

Are the measures the same for both of you? ☐

Why is using body parts not a good way to measure? ☐

☐

Introducing the metre

Because people are different sizes it is important that we measure length with a unit that is the same for everyone. When we measure large things or distances, we use the **metre**.

Parent: Use a tape-measure to cut a length of rope, or thick string, 1 metre long.

Use the **metre rope** as a guide and look around the house to find things which are **longer than 1 metre**, **shorter than 1 metre** or **about the same as 1 metre**, then fill in this table.

Object	Longer than 1 metre	About the same as 1 metre	Shorter than 1 metre

Now measure the following things. Use the metre rope and write **taller than**, **shorter than** or **about** in the spaces:

I am

_____

1 metre.

The armchair is

_____

1 metre.

The table is

_____

1 metre.

The television is

_____

1 metre.

Next, measure the following things. Use the metre rope and write **wider than**, **narrower than**, or **about** in the spaces:

The window is [   ] I metre.

The doorway is [   ] I metre.

■ TEST 4 ■

1 Label the longer skipping rope.

longer

2 Label the shorter straw.

shorter

3 Label the wider car.

wider

---

4 Label the narrower ribbon.

narrower

Find 2 things taller than I metre:

5 [   ]   **6** [   ]

Find 2 things shorter than I metre:

7 [   ]   **8** [   ]

Find 2 things wider than I metre:

9 [   ]

10 [   ]

Find 2 things narrower than I metre:

11 [   ]

12 [   ]

Measuring in centimetres

The metre is too large when we want to measure small items or distances, so it is split up into smaller units called **centimetres**.

There are 100 centimetres in 1 metre. We can write 100 <u>cm.</u>

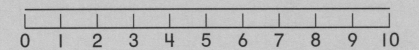

This line is 10 cm long. Cut a length of wool or string the same length and look for different things **taller than 10 cm**, **about 10 cm** and **shorter than 10 cm**. Find 3 things for each column on the chart.

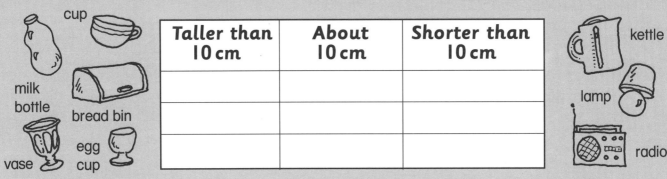

Taller than 10 cm	About 10 cm	Shorter than 10 cm

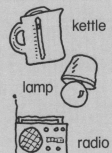

Measuring with a ruler

Rulers are marked in centimetres. When you measure with a ruler make sure the zero on the ruler, and the end of the thing to be measured, are level. Then count along the ruler to the other end of the object to see how long it is.

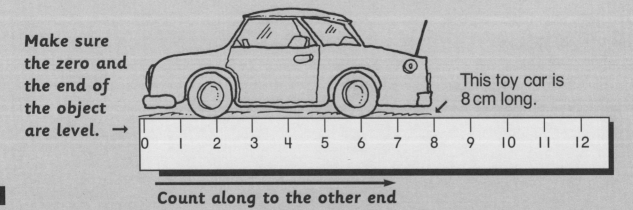

Make sure the zero and the end of the object are level. →

This toy car is 8 cm long.

Count along to the other end

Use a ruler to measure these lines.

_____ [ ] cm _____ [ ] cm

_____ [ ] cm

_____ [ ] cm

_____ [ ] cm

_____ [ ] cm ____ [ ] cm

Draw a line 5 cm long: [   ]

Draw a line 10 cm long: [   ]

Measuring curved lines

To measure a curved line, you can use a piece of string. To do this, lay the string carefully on the curved line making sure the starting ends are level. Use your finger to pinch the string level with the other end of the line. Then transfer the string to a ruler to read off the measurement.

Estimate and measure these lines using a piece of string and a rule.

Estimate [ ] cm

Measure [ ] cm

Estimate [ ] cm

Measure [ ] cm

Area

If you move your hand over this page you are touching the **surface**. The space covered by a **surface** is called **area**.

Colour the circle with the **greater area**.

Colour the square with the **smaller area**.

Cover the **surface** of a small book with pennies to measure the **area**. Try not to leave any spaces.

How many did you use?

Cut out some small squares, all the same size, from a sheet of paper and measure the same area.

How many did you use?

Cut out small triangles, again all the same size, to measure the area again.

How many did you use?

Which shape covered the book best? Why?

Count the squares to find the area of each shape.

 squares   squares   squares   squares   squares

This shape has an area of 7 squares. Colour it and draw and colour shapes with areas of 8, 5, 10 and 6 squares.

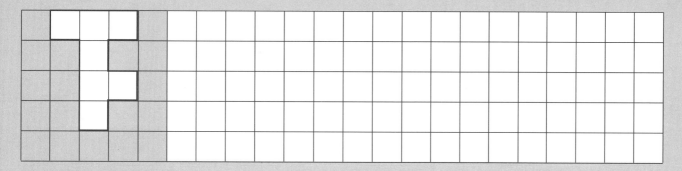

Using cm squared paper, draw around a rubber, a pencil sharpener, and a small book. Count the number of squares in the shape and this will give the area in square centimetres.

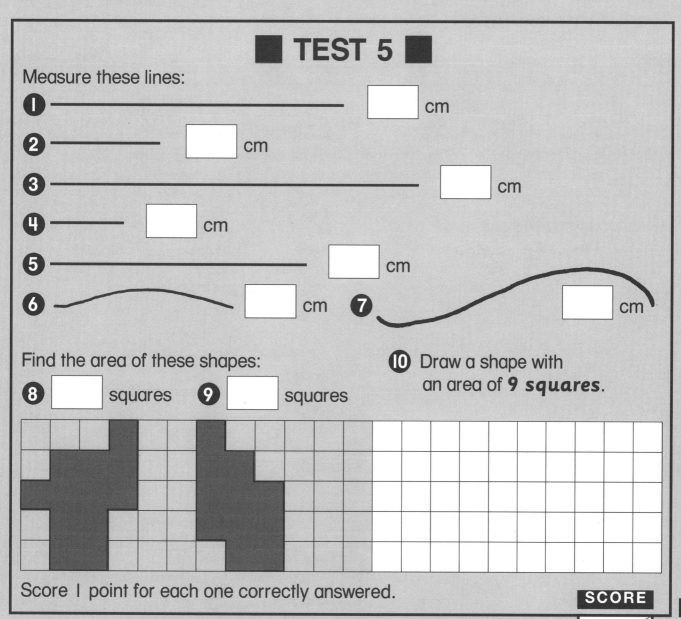

■ **TEST 5** ■

Measure these lines:

1 ———————————————— [ ] cm

2 ———————— [ ] cm

3 ———————————————— [ ] cm

4 ——— [ ] cm

5 ————————————— [ ] cm

6 ~~~~~ [ ] cm   **7** ~~~~~~~~~ [ ] cm

Find the area of these shapes:

8 [ ] squares   **9** [ ] squares

10 Draw a shape with an area of **9 squares**.

Score 1 point for each one correctly answered.

SCORE
/ 10

Capacity

Capacity is the amount a solid container will hold.

You will need: a plastic bottle   a tin   a cup   water

Estimate which holds the most:

I think the [   ] will hold the most water.

Estimate which holds the least:

I think the [   ] will hold the least water.

Find out by pouring from one container to another:

The [   ] holds most. The [   ] holds least.

These are **containers**:   egg cup   small plastic box   plastic bowl   plastic jug

These can be used as
units of measurement: spoon   plastic cup   plastic bottle

Use these containers and units of measurement and fill in the chart:

First make an estimate and then check your answer.

	name of container		amount	unit	
I estimate the	[ ]	will hold	[ ]	[ ]	of water.
I found the	[ ]	will hold	[ ]	[ ]	of water.
I estimate the	[ ]	will hold	[ ]	[ ]	of water.
I found the	[ ]	will hold	[ ]	[ ]	of water.
I estimate the	[ ]	will hold	[ ]	[ ]	of water.
I found the	[ ]	will hold	[ ]	[ ]	of water.

20

Introducing the litre

As with the other ways of measuring, we need a standard unit to measure how much a container will hold. For capacity the unit is **1 litre**. We usually measure liquids in **litres**.

You will need a litre jug and a selection of containers such as

a bowl   a bottle   a bucket   a mug   a biscuit tin

Look at the litre jug. Estimate if each container holds **more than 1 litre**, **less than 1 litre**, or **about 1 litre**.

I estimate

Fill the litre jug with water and check by pouring.

The [**bowl**] holds [**more than**] 1 litre. The [ ] holds [ ] 1 litre.

The [ ] holds [ ] 1 litre. The [ ] holds [ ] 1 litre.

Volume

Volume is the amount of space taken up by a solid shape.

Which shape has the **greater volume** or takes up more space?

Which shape has the **smaller volume** or takes up less space?

Match the labels to the shape:

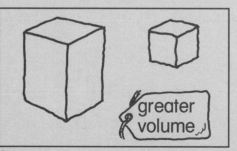

greater volume

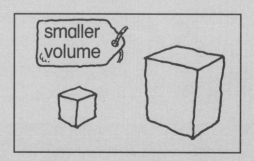

smaller volume

We can use blocks or cubes of the same size to build shapes of a certain **volume**. These are called **unit cubes**.

This shape has a volume of 5 unit cubes. Use sugar cubes, wooden blocks, or cube-shaped building blocks to build shapes with a volume of 8 unit cubes and 10 unit cubes.

■ TEST 6 ■

Weighing
Use the scales to weigh these things:

Weigh ❶ 4 apples ☐ g ❷ 3 onions ☐ g ❸ 2 bananas ☐ g

Weigh out ❹ 6 g rice ❺ 5 g sugar ❻ 10 g pasta

Measuring
Use a ruler to measure these lines:

❼ ─────────────────────── ☐ cm

❽ ────────── ☐ cm ❾ ──────────── ☐ cm

❿ ───────────────────── ☐ cm

You will need string to measure these:

⓫ ☐ cm ⓬ ☐ cm

⓭ What is the area of this shape?

⓮ Draw a shape with an area of 12 squares:

Capacity
⓯ Tick which holds most:

☑

☐

⓰ Tick which holds least:

☐

☑

Volume
⓱ This shape has a volume of ☐10 unit cubes.

⓲ This shape has a volume of ☐9 unit cubes.

RECORD OF SUCCESS

TEST 1
5

TEST 2
8

TEST 3
10

TEST 4
12

TEST 5
10

TEST 6
18

TOTAL
63

* * * * * * * CERTIFICATE * * * * * * *

This is to certify that

_____

has successfully finished this book and has done very well.

signed _____

date _____

Answers

Test 1

1 bus. **2** apple. **3** shoe. **4** brick.

5 Score one point if correct procedure is followed.

Test 2

Score 1 point for each item placed correctly.

Test 3

Score 1 point for each one weighed correctly.

Test 4

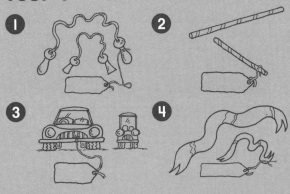

Score 1 point for each item identified correctly which is taller, shorter, wider and narrower than 1 metre.

Test 5

1 8 cm **2** 3 cm **3** 10 cm **4** 2 cm

5 7 cm **6** 5 cm **7** 8 cm

8 12 squares **9** 11 squares

10 Score 1 point for a correct drawing.

Test 6

1 – 6 Score 1 point for each one weighed correctly.

7 8 cm **8** 3 cm **9** 5 cm

10 9 cm **11** 5 cm **12** 7 cm

13 11 squares

14 Score 1 point for a correct drawing.

15

16

17 10 unit cubes. **18** 9 unit cubes.

ISBN 0 340 62985 1
Text copyright © 1996 Rhona Whiteford and Jim Fitzsimmons
Illustrations copyright © 1996 Sascha Lipscomb

The rights of Rhona Whiteford and Jim Fitzsimmons to be identified as the authors of this work has been asserted by them in accordance with the Copyright, Design and Patent Act 1988.

First published in Great Britain 1996

10 9 8 7 6 5 4 3 2 1

Published by Hodder Children's Books, a division of Hodder Headline plc, 338 Euston Road, London NW1 3BH.

A CIP record is registered by and held at the British Library.

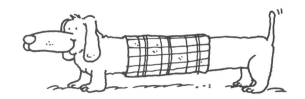